JOHN THOMPSON'S
EASIEST PIANO COURSE
FIRST PIANO DUETS

Ring-A-Ring O' Roses 3
Little Bird 4
Banks Of The Ohio 5
Pussy Cat, Pussy Cat 6
This Old Man 8
Frère Jacques 8
Hot Cross Buns 10
Kum Ba Yah 10
We Three Kings 12
Jingle Bells 14
Land Of Hope And Glory 16
Twinkle, Twinkle, Little Star 18
I Saw Three Ships 18
Ode To Joy 20
We Wish You A Merry Christmas 22
The Elephant 24
Country Gardens 26
The Blue Danube 28
The Merry Peasant 30

Teachers and Parents

This collection of duets is intended as
supplementary material for those working through
John Thompson's Easiest Piano Course Parts 2 and 3.
The pieces may also be used for sight reading practice
by more advanced students.
The material is not specifically graded, although
pieces appearing later in the book tend to be more
demanding than the earlier ones. The first three tunes
are for the right hand only, and thereafter
both hands are employed.
Dynamics, phrasing and tempo indications have been
deliberately omitted, since they are not introduced
until Part Three of the Easiest Piano Course,
and initially the student's attention should be focused
on playing notes and rhythms accurately.
Outline fingering has been included in the pupil's
part, and in general the hand is assumed to remain in
a five-finger position until a new fingering indicates a
position shift. The fingering should suit most hands,
although logical alternatives are always possible.

Illustrations by xheight Limited
Music setting by Stave Origination
Printed and bound in the United Kingdom by
Caligraving Limited, Thetford, Norfolk.

Exclusive distributors:
Music Sales Limited,
14/15 Berners Street, London W1T 3LJ

Order No. WMR000209

Parts 1+2

Ring-A-Ring O' Roses

Little Bird

Part 1 (Pupil)

Traditional

Part 2

Banks of the Ohio

Part 1 (Pupil)

Traditional

Part 2

Pussy Cat, Pussy Cat

Traditional

Pussy Cat, Pussy Cat

Traditional

This Old Man

Traditional

Frère Jacques

Traditional

This Old Man

Traditional

Frère Jacques

Traditional

Hot Cross Buns

Traditional

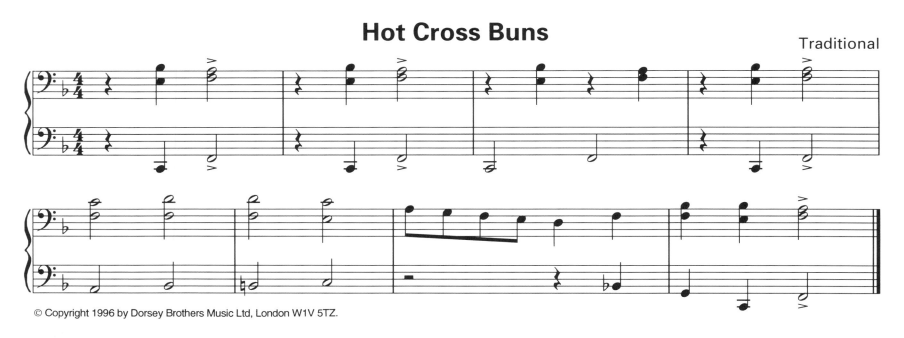

Kum Ba Yah

Traditional

Hot Cross Buns

Traditional

Kum Ba Yah

Traditional

We Three Kings

J.H. Hopkins

Part 1 (Pupil)

We Three Kings

J.H. Hopkins

Jingle Bells

J. Pierpont

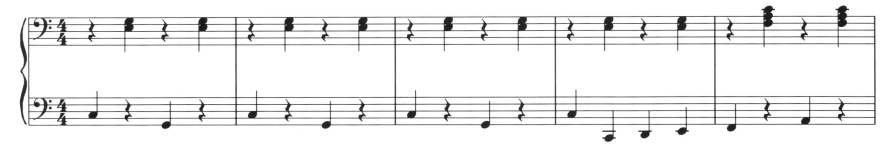

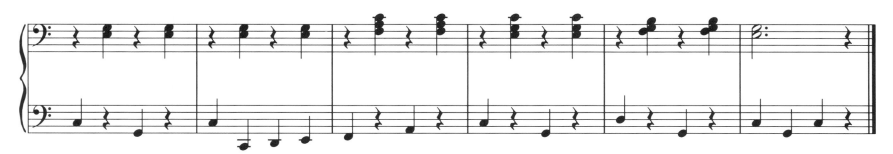

Jingle Bells

J. Pierpont

Play either the right hand or the left hand — or even both together!

Land of Hope and Glory

Edward Elgar

Part 1 (Pupil)

Land of Hope and Glory

Edward Elgar

Twinkle, Twinkle, Little Star

Traditional

I Saw Three Ships

Traditional

Twinkle, Twinkle, Little Star

Traditional

Play the notes under the 8va sign an octave higher.

I Saw Three Ships

Traditional

Ode to Joy

Ludwig van Beethoven

Ode to Joy

Ludwig van Beethoven

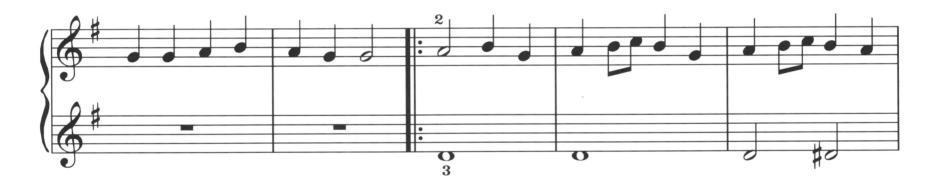

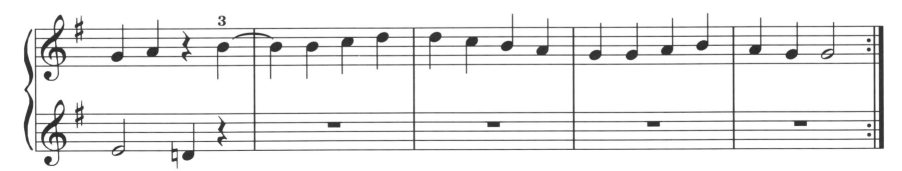

We Wish You a Merry Christmas

Traditional

We Wish You a Merry Christmas

Traditional

The Elephant

Camille Saint-Saëns

This part may be played an octave lower if you wish.

The Elephant

Camille Saint-Saëns

Part 2

Country Gardens

Traditional

Country Gardens

Traditional

The Blue Danube

Johann Strauss II

The Blue Danube

Johann Strauss II

The Merry Peasant

Robert Schumann

In this piece the pupil may play either part.

The Merry Peasant

Robert Schumann

In this piece the pupil may play either part.